A Celebration of You

Place your photo here

This book belongs to:

♥ Dear Baby ♥

As soon as we found out about you,
we had so much to tell you.

Turn these pages and take a look
At this, your very special book.
A pleasure to see your life unfold,
A treasure to keep until you're old.

Our very first letter to you:

Dear _____

_____

_____

_____

_____

_____

_____

_____

_____

_____

_____

_____

With lots of love _____

_____

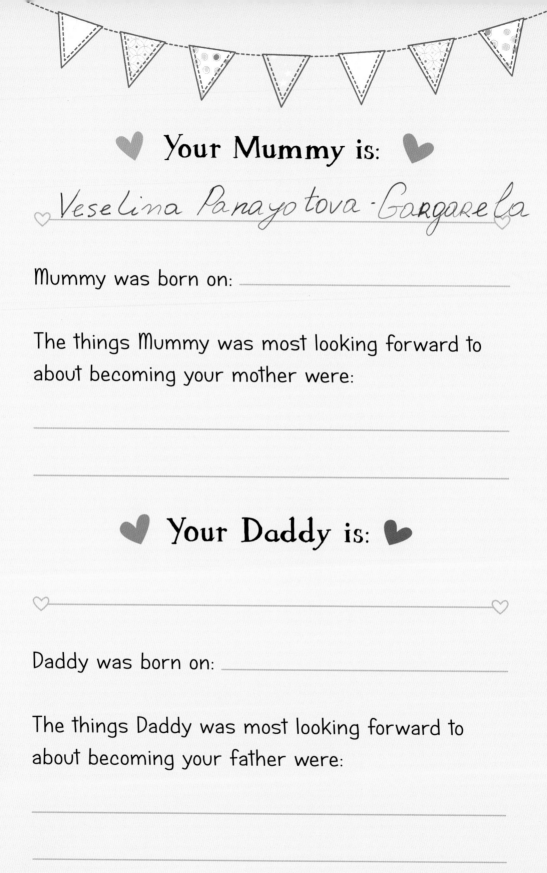

♥ Your Mummy is: ♥

Veselina Panayotova-Gargarela

Mummy was born on: _____

The things Mummy was most looking forward to about becoming your mother were:

_____

_____

♥ Your Daddy is: ♥

_____

Daddy was born on: _____

The things Daddy was most looking forward to about becoming your father were:

_____

_____

Mummy and Daddy first met on:

_____

This is what happened:

_____

This is how Mummy and Daddy looked
before you were born:

Place your photo here

We've changed a lot since then!

Your Fantastic ★ Family ♥

Before you were born,
this was your family:

Place your photo here

The love of your family
is one of life's great gifts.

Place your photo here

Place your photo here

Family Tree

Mum's Mum

Mum's Dad

Mum

Brothers

Sisters

Adding your name to our family tree,
Makes us as happy as parents can be!

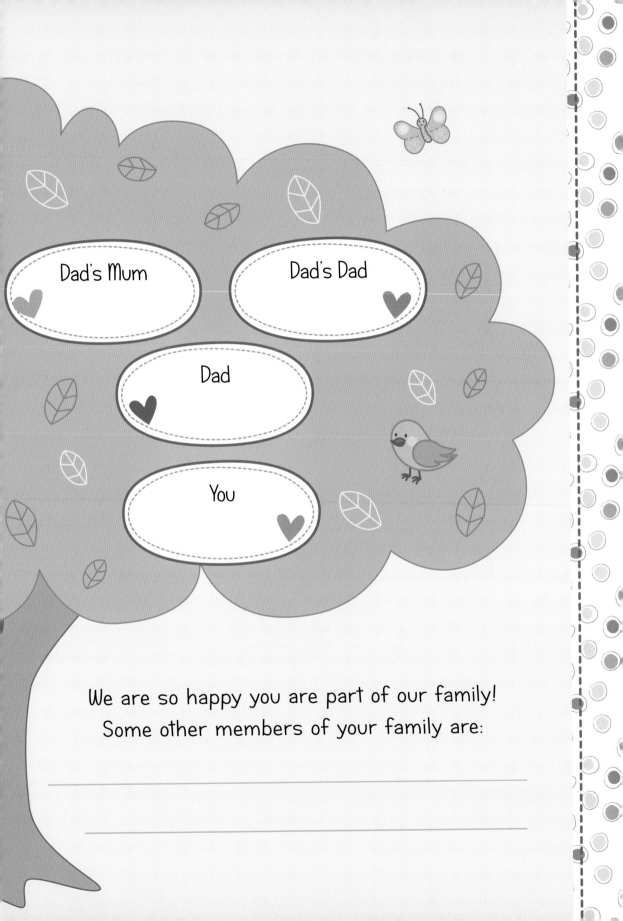

Dad's Mum

Dad's Dad

Dad

You

We are so happy you are part of our family!
Some other members of your family are:

_____

_____

Before You Were Born

Exciting News

Mummy found out she was expecting you on:

When Mummy found out the news,
the first thing she did was:

Jump high 😄. Send a photo of the positive
test to your granny. Then jump and scream again
Then cry a bit

Mummy was most excited about:

Having you 💕 😊

Finding out we were having you,
Made each and every wish come true.

When Daddy found out the news,
the first thing he did was:

_____

_____

_____

Daddy was most excited about:

_____

_____

_____

We couldn't wait to tell our family and friends
the wonderful news! The first people we told were:

Баба Дани

_____

And this is what they said:

- Оу... Страхотно 😄 Поздравления

_____

The First Time We Saw You

Mummy had her first ultrasound scan on:

It took place at:

Ashcombe Clinic, WsM

This is what we thought when we first saw you:

I was amazed. Не можех да повярвам че си в коремчето ми 😊

You were this big:

The first person we showed your picture to was:

Everyone, but first Баба Дани, Вики (Agu)

Even though we couldn't touch,
We already loved you oh so much!

Place your photo here

Ultrasound Photos

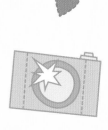

These are pictures from your other scans:

Place your photo here

We saw your picture on the screen-
The most beautiful thing we'd ever seen!

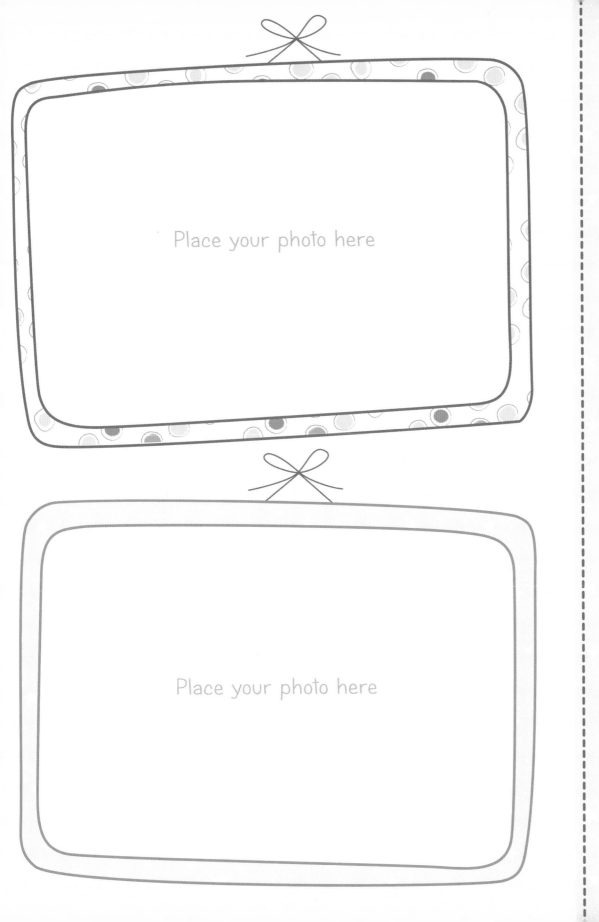

Place your photo here

Place your photo here

Growing Inside Mummy

When Mummy was pregnant, she liked to eat:

"Healthy" fruit, veg., pickles, cooked food, cheese on toast ...

. . . but not:

...

Mummy first felt you kick on:

This was amazing. You kicked mostly at night

Your favourite time for kicking was:

Нощна птичка, през деня кротуваш, вечер буйстваш

This is Mummy . . .

. . . at three months:

Place your
photo here

. . . at six months:

Place your
photo here

. . . just before you were born!

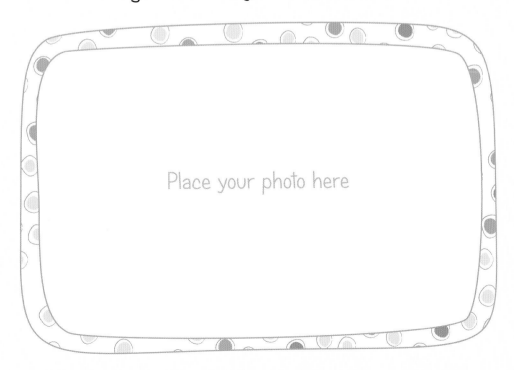

Place your photo here

Getting Ready for Baby!

The very first thing we bought for you was:

Cot bed + beautiful bedding + cute baby shoes

Some other things we got ready
before you arrived were:

Your Chicco Artic push chair (Daddy got it
from Ebay)Та ти е от Лампи и Мимето

Баба Дани даде £200,с които купих много бебешки
неща, орешки и още красиви гардероб cета :)

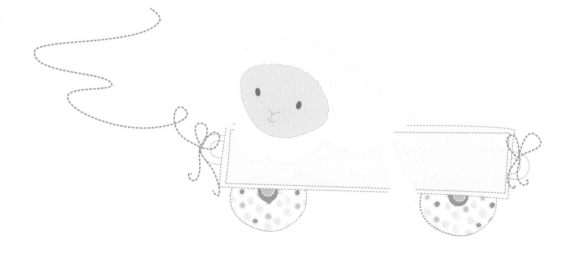

We learned all about babies at these classes:
YouTube, Antenatal Class

Mummy was surprised to find out that:

Daddy was surprised to find out that:

We made these new friends:

Waiting for our baby,
Deciding what you'll need:
Muslins, nappies, toys and clothes
And bottles for your feed!

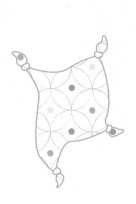

Cuddle You Cosy

We wanted you to be cosy
and comfy when you arrived!

Here are some of the snuggly
things we bought for you:

You had this many blankets:

_____

You had this many cuddly toys:

_____

 You had this many booties:

_____

You had this many sleepsuits:

_____

 Snuggle up, baby, cuddle you tight.
We'll keep you cosy all through the night!

Happy Home

Your room was decorated in this colour:

_____

It took us this long:

_____

We put these pictures on the walls:

_____

These are some other things we bought
for your room:

_____

_____

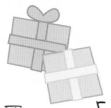 You were given these special gifts
from our friends and family:

Тази книга ти е от бате Борко и Кака Таня.

_____

_____

This is a photo of your room:

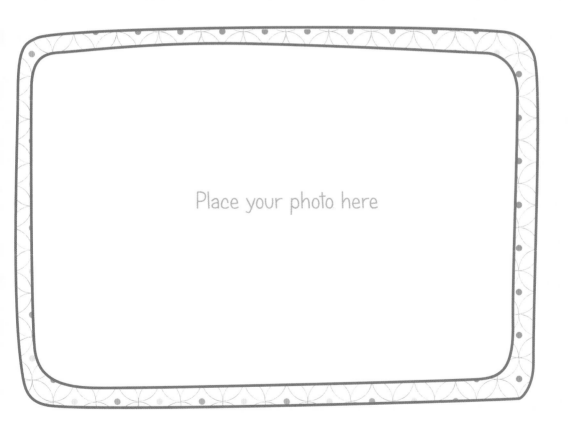

Place your photo here

Bedtime, baby, time to rest.
We hope you like your cosy nest!

Your Own Special Name

Mummy thought you would be:

 a girl

 a boy

Daddy thought you would be:

 a girl

a boy

A name is a parent's first gift to their child.

Your name was chosen especially for you!

Mummy liked these names:

Любен, - да е обичан
дългоочаквана мъжка рожба
Мотчил - да е радост за родителите ти
Ангел - На чичо ти Анбо, който запозна
мама и тати

Daddy liked these names:

Георги

It took Mummy and Daddy this long to decide on your name:

Почти 9 месеца ☺

Hello,
Baby!

Hello, Baby!

You were born at:

The date was:

The time was:

It took this long for you to be born:

These people were at your birth:

_____

_____

_____

When Mummy first saw you,
this is what she did:

_____

_____

When Daddy first saw you,
this is what he did:

_____

_____

The first person we told about your birth was:

_____

Welcome to the world!

Beautiful Baby!

This is the first ever photograph of you:

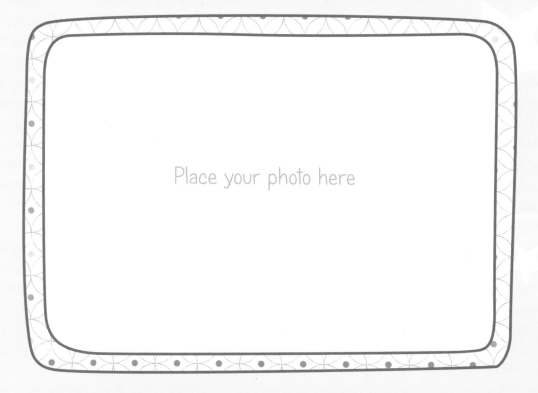

Place your photo here

Ten tiny fingers, ten tiny toes,
Two chubby cheeks and one tiny nose,
Two little eyes and two little ears,
One little baby, finally here!

The colour of your hair: Руса

The colour of your eyes: Сиво-Сини

Your weight: 3.62 кг

Your length: _____

Your head circumference: _____

The name we gave you was:

Любен

Your name means:
С това име те орисваме да бъдеш
обичан и щастлив. Също така си кръстен на
татко си Любомир, който много те обича ☺

We chose this special name because:

_____

_____

Picture Perfect!

These pictures show your very first moments:

Place your photo here

Place your photo here

Place your photo here

Welcome to the Family

Mummy looked
like this
when she
was a baby.

Place your photo here

Place your photo here

Daddy looked
like this
when he
was a baby.

We know you little, we love you lots.
Our love for you would fill ten pots.
Fifteen buckets, sixteen cans,
Three teacups and four dishpans.

When you were born you looked most like:

Ангела ххх

But you also looked a bit like:

малко костенурче

Tiny Fingers and Tiny Toes

These are your first handprints:

Tiny hands and tiny feet,
Tiny baby, oh so sweet!

These are your first footprints:

The Day You Were Born

The weather on the day you were born was:

_____

These were some of the things
happening in the world:

_____

_____

_____

_____

We will remember forever the
day you entered the world!

These are some newspaper cuttings
from the day you were born:

Place your cuttings here

Marvellous Memories

These important things happened
in the year you were born:

_____

_____

_____

Mummy and Daddy watched these films:

_____

_____

Mummy and Daddy enjoyed these
television programmes:

_____

_____

Mummy and Daddy listened to these songs:

_____

_____

Daddy's favourite band was called:

_____

Mummy's favourite film star was:

_____

A carton of milk cost: _____

A loaf of bread cost: _____

A newspaper cost: _____

This is what a postage stamp looked like:

Place
your
stamp
here

Smile for the Camera!

We took lots of photographs of you.
These are some of our favourites:

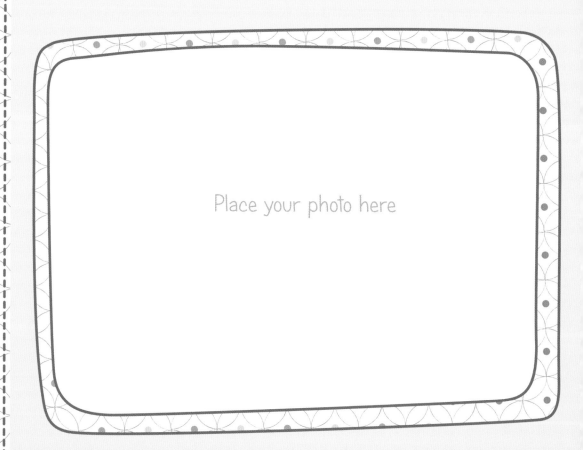

Place your photo here

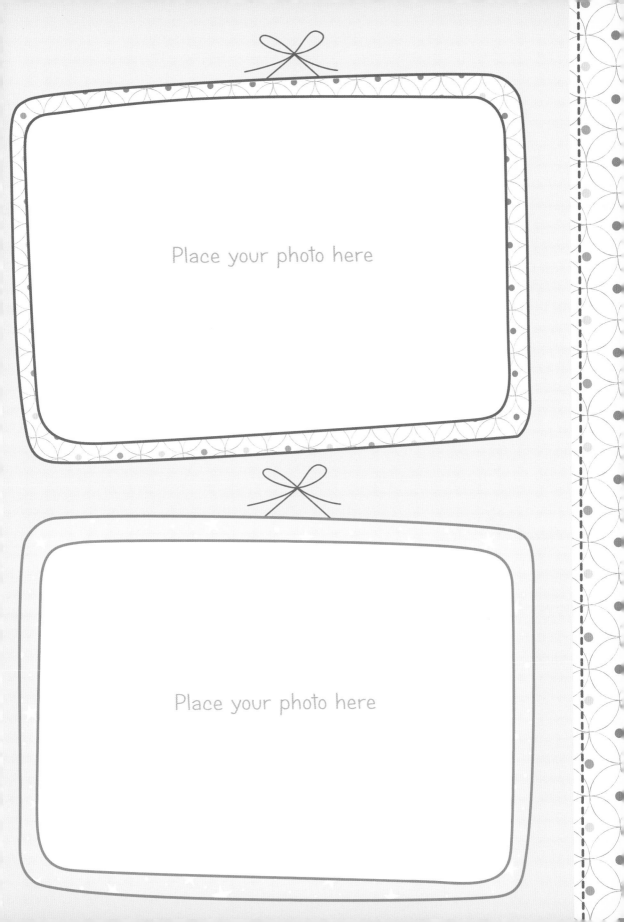

Place your photo here

Place your photo here

Getting to Know You

Home Sweet Home

You came home on:

_____

These are the clothes you were wearing:

_____

_____

 This is how you travelled:

_____

The weather was:

_____

 We'll never forget that special day

When you came home with us to stay!

 Your first address was:

_____

_____

These are the people who lived there:

_____

_____

This is what happened on the first day
we brought you home:

_____

_____

_____

First Night

This is where you slept on your first night at home:

_____

_____

You slept for: ☐ hours

Mummy and Daddy slept for: ☐ hours

Sleep my child and peace attend thee.
All through the night . . .

You slept with these toys:

_____

These are some things Mummy and
Daddy tried to help you sleep:

_____

_____

_____

Celebrating Your Birth

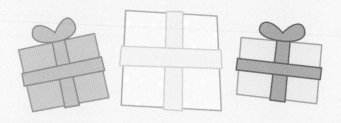

Here are some of the gifts you were given:

_____

_____

_____

_____

Baby girl or baby boy,
A newborn babe brings so much joy!

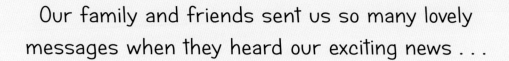

Our family and friends sent us so many lovely messages when they heard our exciting news . . .

Here are some of our favourites:

Warm Wishes

The first people you met were:

_____

_____

_____

_____

This is what they said about you:

_____

_____

_____

_____

_____

_____

_____

Other family and friends who came to visit were:

_____

_____

_____

_____

Family and friends from near and far
Can't wait to meet our brand new star.
Our precious child that shines so bright,
And fills us all with such delight!

Amazing Arrival

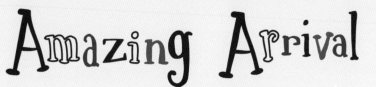

We wanted to tell everyone our
wonderful news!

This is how we announced your birth:

_____

_____

_____

Place your announcement here

These are some of the replies we received:

Splish! Splash!

The first time you had a bath was:

_____

You were given the bath by:

_____

This is what you felt about your first bath:

_____

_____

These were some of your favourite bath toys:

_____

_____

This is a picture of you in the bath:

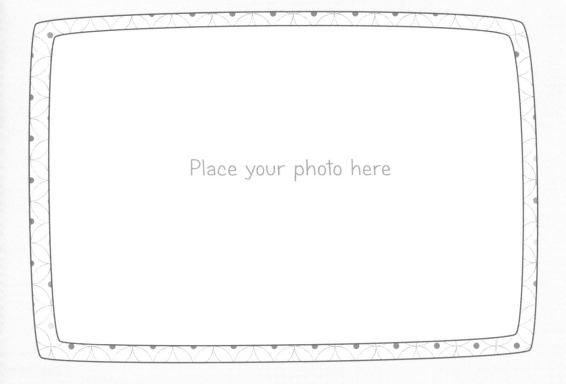

Place your photo here

Time for a bath -
Rub-a-dub-dub!
Splish, splash, splosh
In the bubbly tub!

Day By Day

This was your daily routine when
you were _____ old.

You fed at:

_____

You slept at:

_____

Your favourite time for a cuddle was:

_____

Your favourite time for a story was:

 _____

Baby's Day

Morning:

_____

_____

Lunchtime:

_____

_____

Afternoon:

_____

_____

Evening:

_____

_____

Night:

_____

_____

One Week Old

This is you when you were one week old:

Place your photo here

Look how much you had already grown!

In your first week you wore these clothes:

_____

_____

You enjoyed these activities:

_____

_____

You spent time with these people:

_____

_____

Our favourite memories of your first week are:

_____

_____

_____

Growth Chart

Date	Age

Look how quickly you grew!

Height	Weight

Perfect Pictures

These are some of our favourite pictures of you:

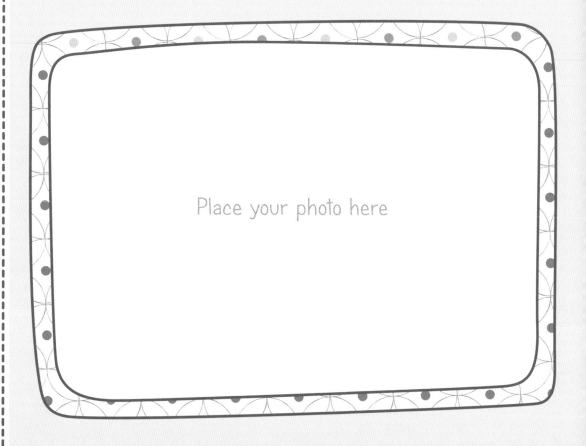

Place your photo here

We love every funny wiggle,
Every gurgle, every giggle.
We love everything you do,
But most of all we just love you!

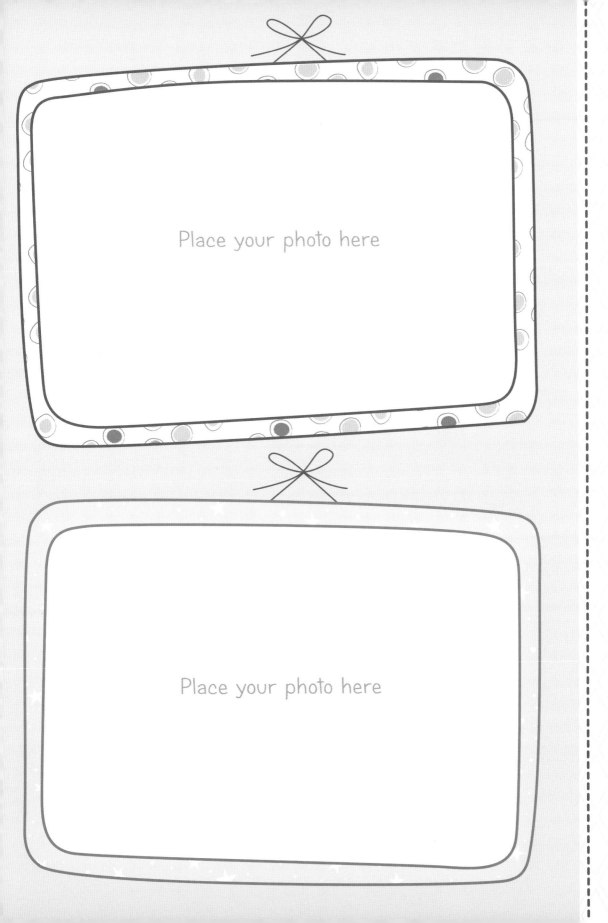

Place your photo here

Place your photo here

Fantastic Firsts

Fantastic Firsts

The first time you smiled was:

_____

You smiled at this person:

_____

Here is a picture of your gorgeous smile:

Place your photo here

The first time you laughed was:

_____

This is what made you laugh:

_____

_____

Tickle your hands and tickle your feet,
Those sparkling smiles are oh-so-sweet!

First Month

These are some photographs of you
in your first month:

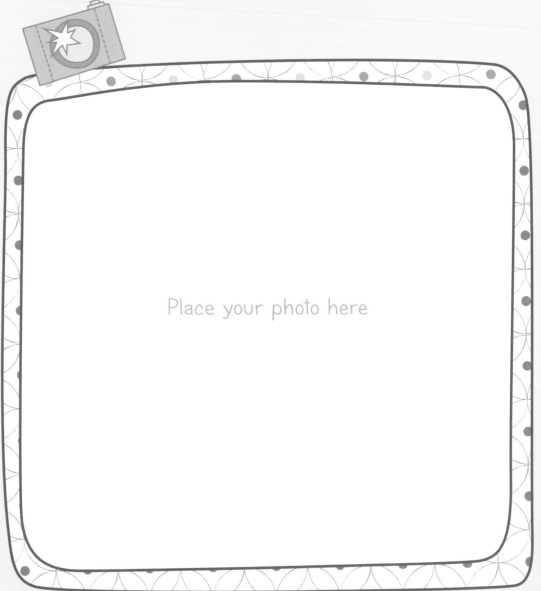

Place your photo here

Place your photo here

Place your photo here

So many moments
Filled with emotion,
Squeezing our hearts
With love and devotion.

Even More Firsts

You first slept through the night
when you were this old:

_____

You rolled over by yourself
for the first time:

_____

 You first discovered your hands:

_____

Your first tooth came through:

_____

You first waved:

_____

You first sat up all by yourself:

_____

You first crawled:

_____

These are some of your other firsts:

_____

_____

_____

We learned something new
each day we spent with you.

Marvellous Mealtimes

You tried your first meal when you were this old:

_____

This is where you sat:

_____

Your meal was cooked by:

_____

This is what you ate:

_____

_____

You were fed by:

_____

This is what you thought of your first meal:

_____

_____

_____

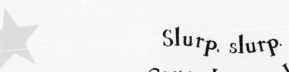

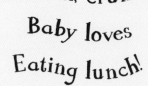

Slurp, slurp.
Crunch, crunch!
Baby loves
Eating lunch!

Fantastic Food

The first solid food you ate was:

_____

The first time you sipped from a cup was:

_____

The first time you fed yourself was:

_____

 Your favourite foods were:

_____

_____

You didn't like:

_____

_____

This is a picture of you eating:

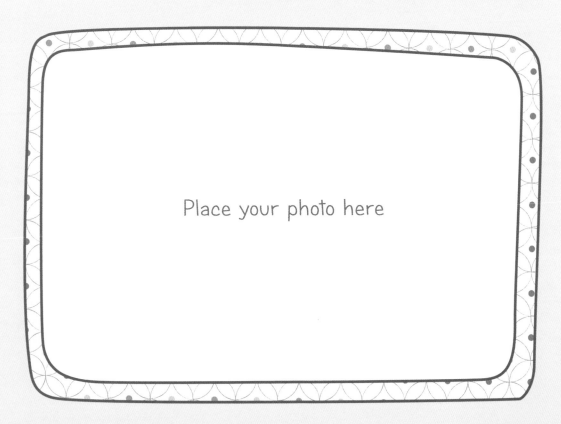

Place your photo here

Out and About

Our first outing was on:

_____

This is where we went:

_____

_____

This is what we did:

_____

_____

_____

The first time you rode in a buggy was:

This is a picture of you in the buggy:

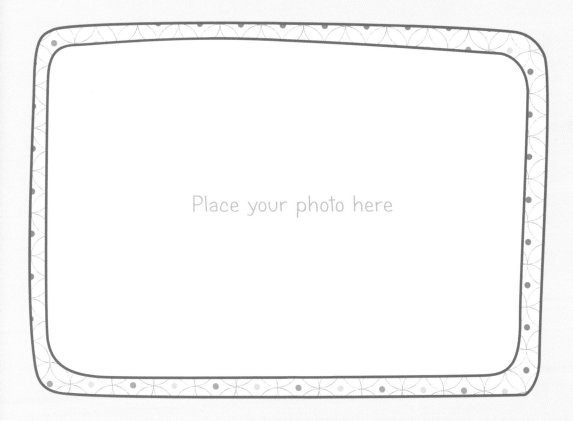

Place your photo here

During the first years of your baby's life, every outing is an adventure.

First Trip Away From Home

Your first time away from
Mummy and Daddy was on:

_____

You stayed with:

_____

These are some of the exciting
things that happened:

_____

_____

_____

This is what we did:

_____

This is what Mummy packed for you:

_____

This is how many toys you took with you:

_____

See you soon!

Even if we're far apart,
You're always present in my heart.

First Holiday

This is where we went on your first holiday:

_____

This is what we packed:

_____

_____

We travelled by:

 _____

The journey took this long:

_____

On holiday, we did these new things:

_____

_____

_____

This is what you liked doing best:

_____

_____

_____

_____

Happy Holidays

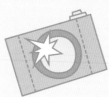

These are some photographs
of your first holiday:

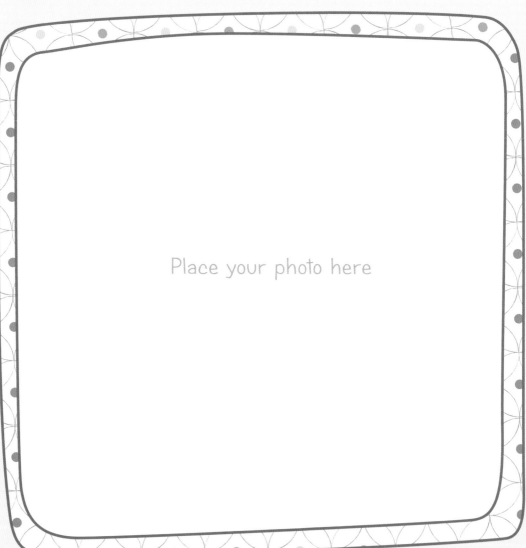

Place your photo here

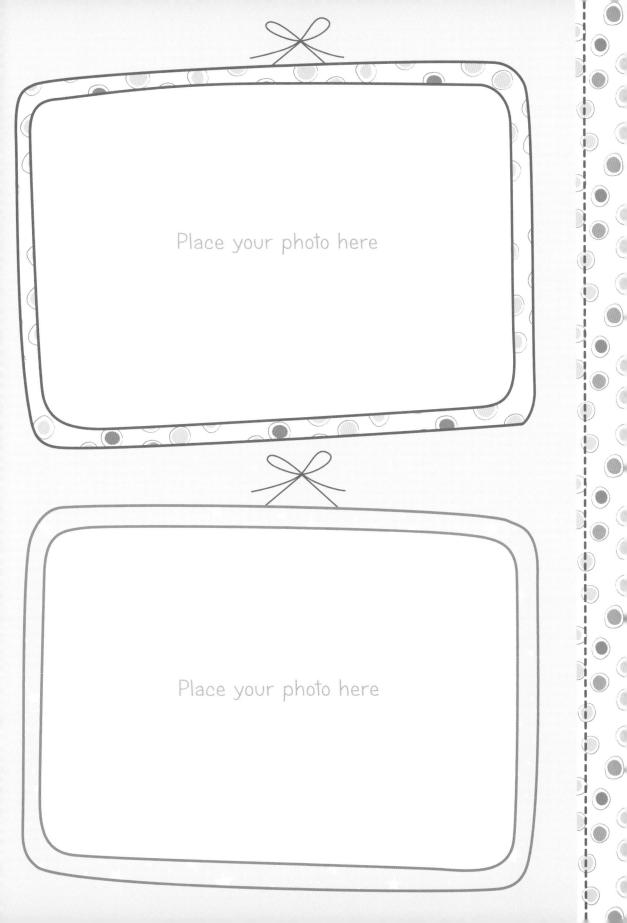

Place your photo here

Place your photo here

Shopping Time

The first outfit we bought you was:

_____

Your first pair of shoes were this size:

_____

And this colour:

_____

Other things we bought were:

_____

_____

_____

We went to the shops,
For everyone knows
That babies grow quickly,
And need lots of clothes!

Your first haircut was on:

_____

_____

This is a little lock of your hair:

First Christmas

You spent your first Christmas at:

_____

You wore this outfit:

_____

_____

 These people were there:

_____

_____

_____

_____

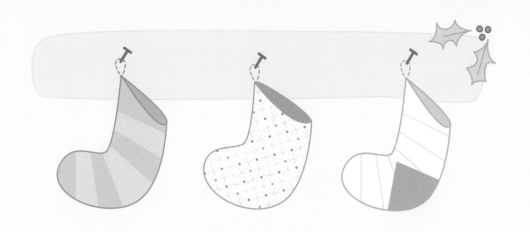

These were some of your favourite presents:

_____

_____

_____

_____

Festive Fun

These are some photographs
of your first Christmas:

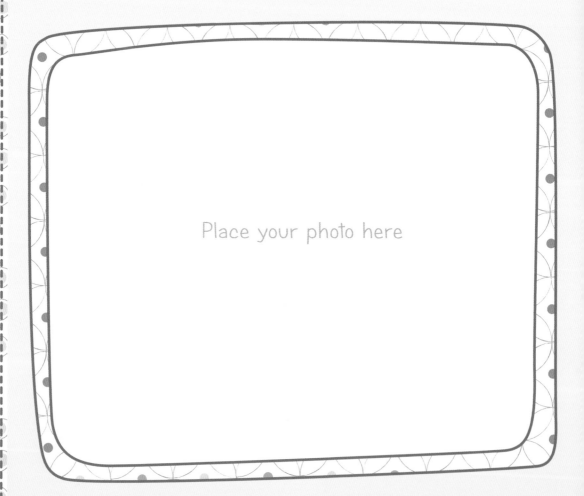

Place your photo here

Place your photo here

Place your photo here

First Words

Your very first word was:

_____

You were this old:

_____

The first time you said 'Mummy' was:

_____

The first time you said 'Daddy' was:

_____

Here are some of your other first words:

Word or sound:	This meant:

Hearing you speak your new words aloud,
Made Mummy and Daddy incredibly proud!

First Steps

You first stood up on your own on:

_____

You took your first steps with support on:

_____

You took your first steps alone on:

_____

Your first steps were watched by:

_____

This is how they reacted:

_____

This picture shows you walking:

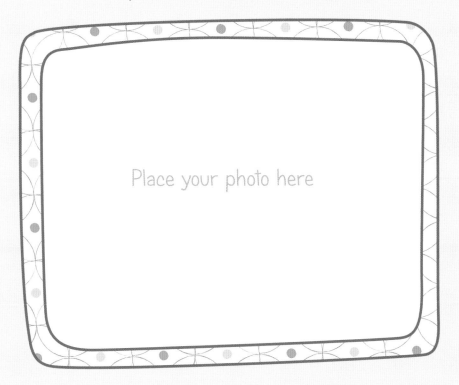

Place your photo here

Learning how to jump and run.
Those tiny feet are full of fun!

The First Year

The First Year

This is a picture of you at the end of your first year:

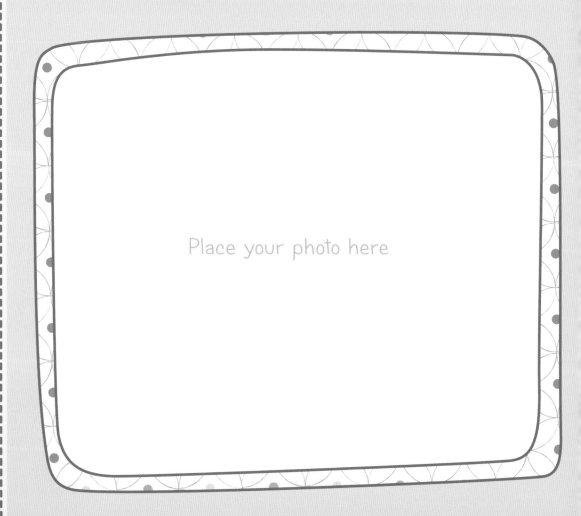

Place your photo here

Your hair colour was:

Your eyes were:

Your weight:

Your height:

You liked playing these games:

These were your favourite toys:

 _____

Your First Birthday

This is what you did on your first birthday:

_____

_____

_____

These were your guests:

_____

_____

_____

This is what we had to eat:

_____

_____

_____

 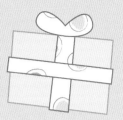

These are some of the
presents you were given:

_____

_____

_____

Your favourite present was:

_____

This is a picture of your birthday cake:

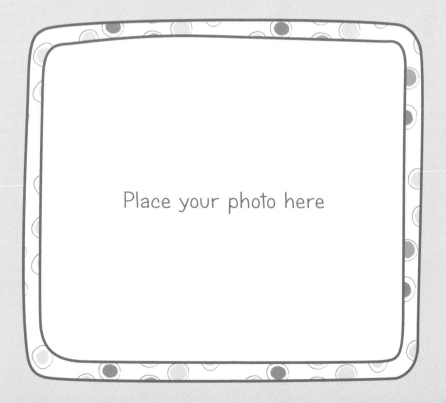

Place your photo here

Beautiful Birthday Baby

Congratulations - you are one!

These are some pictures of you
on your special day:

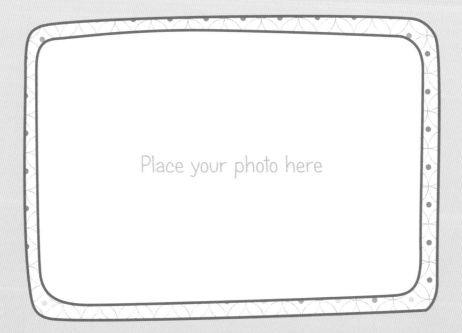

Place your photo here

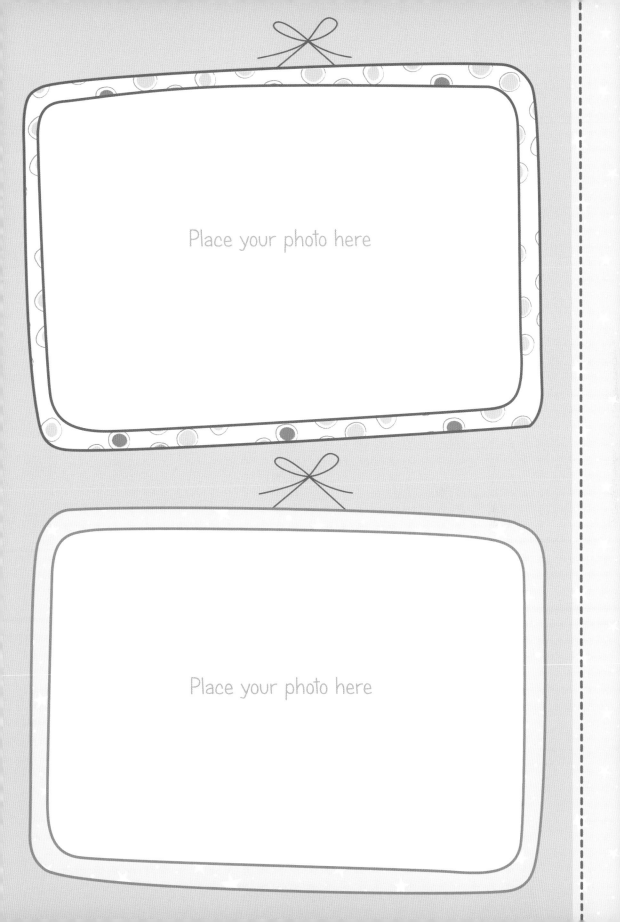

Handprints

These are your handprints at one year old:

Footprints

These are your footprints at one year old:

Special Friends

Your godfather is called:

_____

Your godmother is called:

_____

We chose these special friends
for you because:

_____

_____

_____

Babies fill the world with joy.

These are some pictures of you
with your special friends:

Place your photo here

Place your photo here

Learning About Life

In your first year, you learned to:

_____

Mummy was most proud of:

_____

_____

Daddy was most proud of:

_____

_____

These are some things Mummy
learned to do in your first year:

_____

_____

These are some things Daddy
learned to do in your first year:

_____

_____

We have so many lovely memories of your first
year. These are some of our favourites:

_____

_____

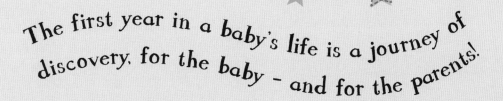

The first year in a baby's life is a journey of
discovery, for the baby – and for the parents!

Magical Moments

Magical Moments

We have shared so many
precious moments with you.

These were some of them:

_____

_____

_____

_____

_____

_____

Our family and friends have written
some special messages for you:

Name:

Message:

Name:

Message:

Name:

Message:

Name:

Message:

Your Second Birthday

This is a picture of you on your second birthday:

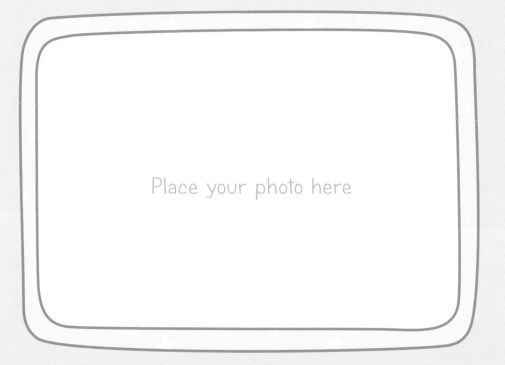

Place your photo here

This is what you did on your second birthday:

_____

_____

These are some of the presents
you were given:

_____

_____

_____

_____

This is what we had to eat:

_____

_____

_____

_____

Open up your sleepy eyes,
it's time for us to say,
Happy Birthday, Baby -
you're two years old today!

Fun
and
Games

These were some of your favourite indoor games:

_____

_____

_____

These were some of your favourite
outdoor games:

_____

_____

_____

_____

Your favourite people to play with were:

_____

_____

_____

_____

Your favourite toy was:

_____

Hey diddle diddle, the cat and the fiddle.
The cow jumped over the moon.
The little dog laughed to see such fun,
And the dish ran away with the spoon.

Marvellous Music

We loved singing songs to you.

These songs made you giggle:

_____

_____

These songs made you sleepy:

_____

_____

You liked to join in with these songs:

_____

_____

You liked to dance to these songs:

_____

_____

These were some of your favourite
songs and nursery rhymes:

_____

_____

_____

_____

_____

_____

Sing a song of sixpence, a pocket full of rye.
Four-and-twenty blackbirds baked in a pie.
When the pie was opened, the birds began to sing.
Wasn't that a dainty dish to set before the king?

Night Night, Sleep Tight

We did these things to get ready for bed:

_____

Your special toy or blanket was:

_____

Your favourite bedtime stories were:

_____

_____

_____

_____

The man in the moon
Looked out of the moon
And this is what he said:
"'Tis time that, now I'm getting up,
All babies went to bed!"

Photos

These are some photos that show
you getting bigger and bigger:

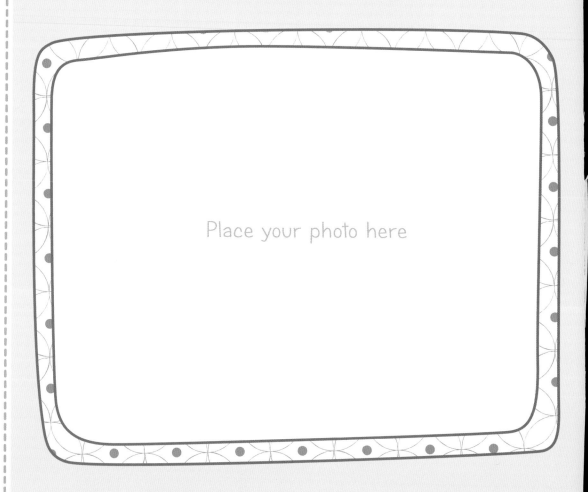

Place your photo here

Babies are sometimes a handful,
but always a heartful!

Place your photo here

Place your photo here

Dreams For You

 We love you because:

_____

_____

_____

_____

 You delight us because:

_____

_____

_____

_____

These are our hopes and dreams for you:

We have a special wish for you -
May all your hopes and dreams come true.

LITTLE TIGER PRESS
1 The Coda Centre, 189 Munster Road, London SW6 6AW
www.littletiger.co.uk

First published in Great Britain 2013

Text and illustrations copyright © Little Tiger Press 2013
Illustrations by Melissa Four
A CIP catalogue record for this book is available from the British Library

All rights reserved • ISBN 978-1-84895-706-0
Printed in Heshan, China • LTP/1800/0660/0513

2 4 6 8 10 9 7 5 3 1